Mariposa's Wish

Story by
Nancy Littlefield

Illustrations by
Carol Meckling

Carol Meckling

To Mom, who taught me the fascination of nature. - N.L.

Mariposa'a Wish
Text copyright © 2019 Nancy Littlefield
Illustrations copyright © 2019 Carol Meckling
ISBN 13: 978-1-7332142-0-9

Published By
Nancy Littlefield
mariposaswish@gmail.com

Monarchs always lay their eggs on milkweed plants.

Summer sunshine

warms a grassy meadow.
Beneath a thick milkweed leaf
sits a tiny egg. Inside is a
caterpillar named **Mariposa**.

For something so young and small,
Mariposa makes an astonishing wish:
to go on a journey.

Mariposa nibbles a hole in the shell of her cramped egg.

A newly hatched caterpillar is smaller than a grain of rice.

Once the opening is big enough, out she creeps. The rest of her shell is her first meal.

Mariposa tastes the milkweed leaf.
It's perfect: crunchy,
juicy, and bitter.

Eating milkweed protects monarchs.
It makes them taste bad to
birds and other predators.

Mariposa eats small,
lacy holes in her leaf. Right
now she can barely creep an
inch. At this speed, how far
will she get on her journey?

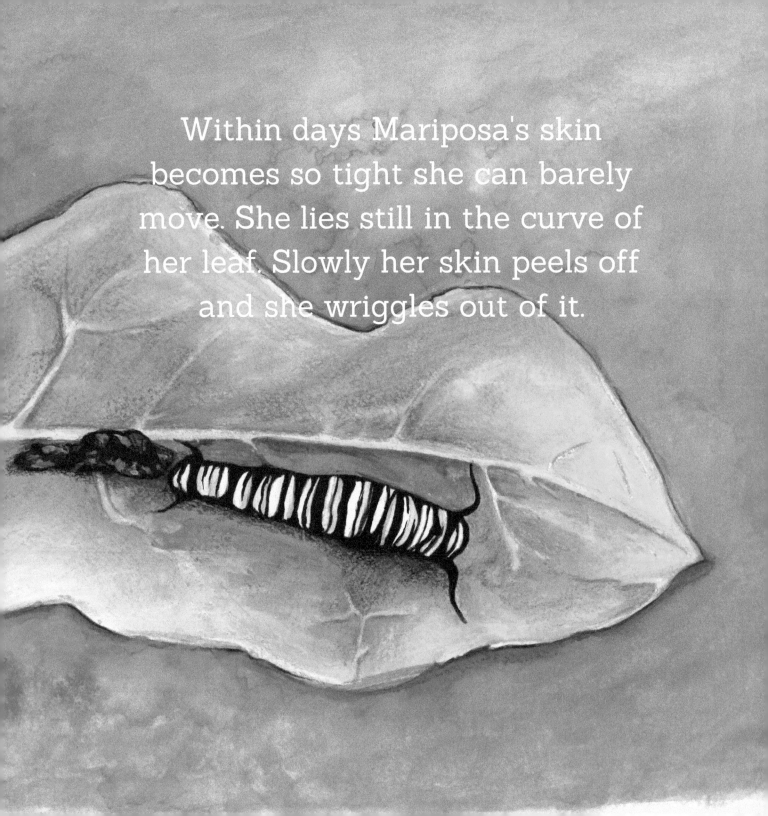

Within days Mariposa's skin becomes so tight she can barely move. She lies still in the curve of her leaf. Slowly her skin peels off and she wriggles out of it.

Mariposa adores the yellow, white, and black stripes on her new skin.

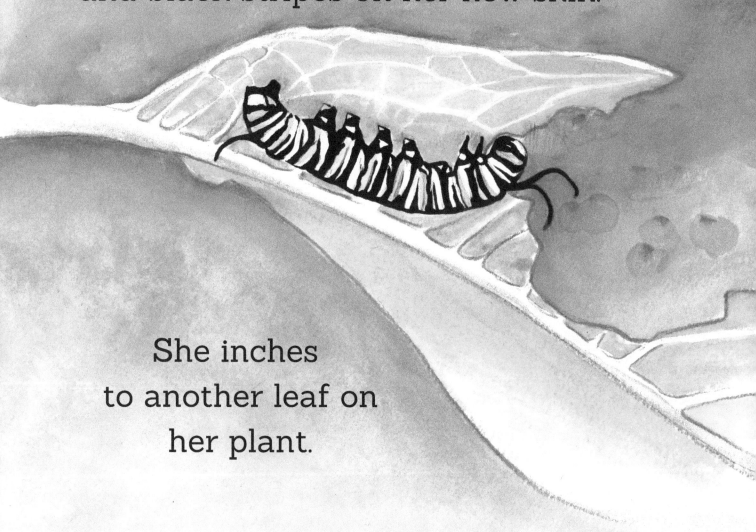

She inches to another leaf on her plant.

For nearly two weeks, Mariposa munches and grows.

A monarch caterpillar grows as large as a child's finger.

Eventually, she can devour entire leaves.

Now that she is bigger, Mariposa explores all around her milkweed plant.

The meadow looks a little different from each leaf. Yet she longs to see more.

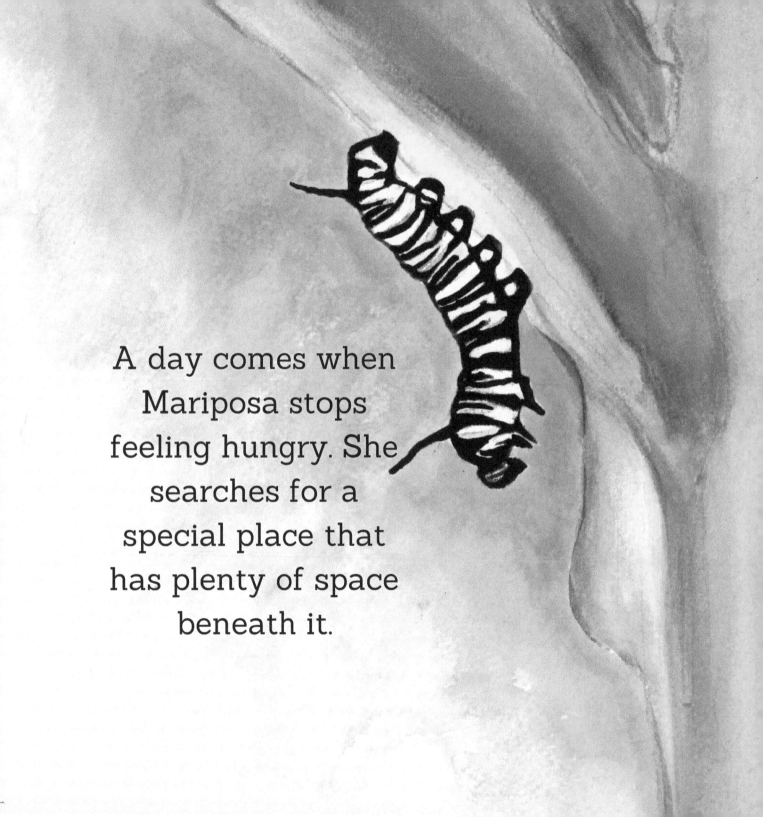

A day comes when
Mariposa stops
feeling hungry. She
searches for a
special place that
has plenty of space
beneath it.

Under a protective leaf,
Mariposa spins silky thread
into a sticky pad. When the
pad is finished, she attaches
herself to it.

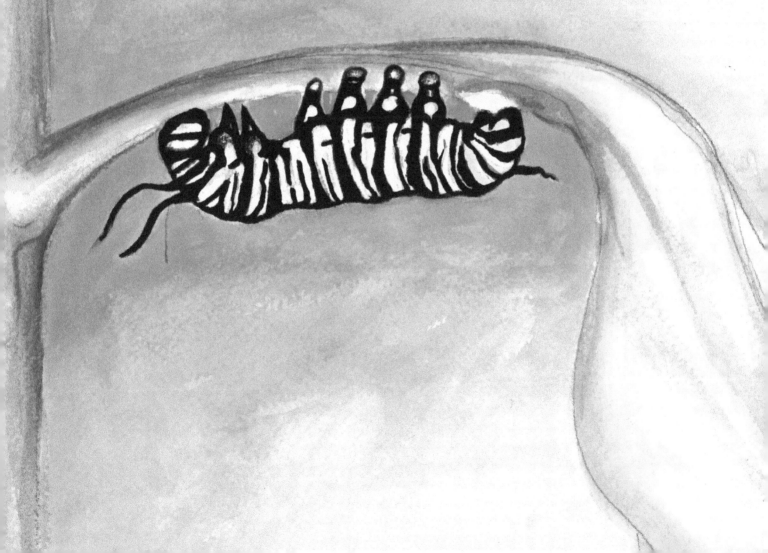

Slowly her legs let go of the leaf, but Mariposa doesn't fall.

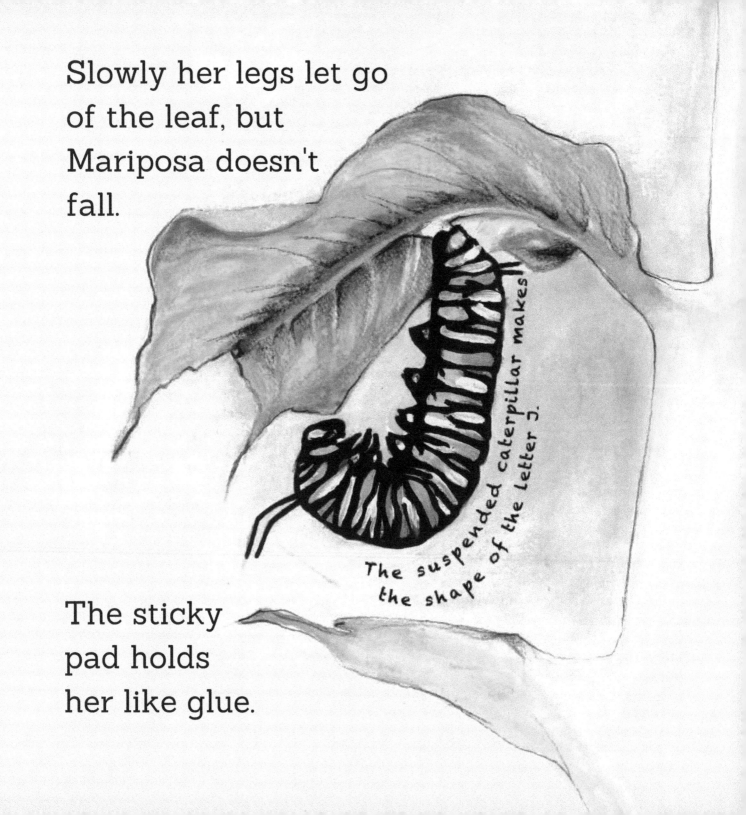

The suspended caterpillar makes the shape of the letter J.

The sticky pad holds her like glue.

In a few hours, Mariposa's skin splits and a green covering wraps her like a puffy blanket.

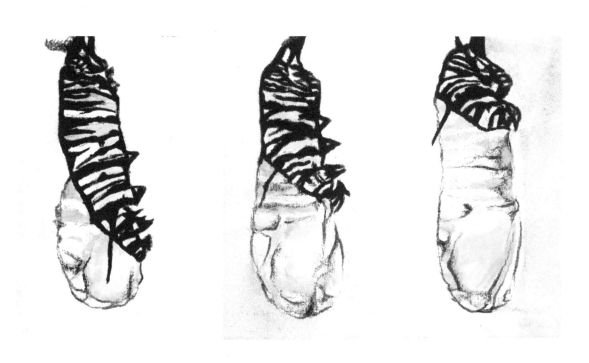

Making a chrysalis is the caterpillar's last molt.

The covering hardens and
smoothes. A few golden
sparkles decorate
Mariposa's lovely chrysalis.

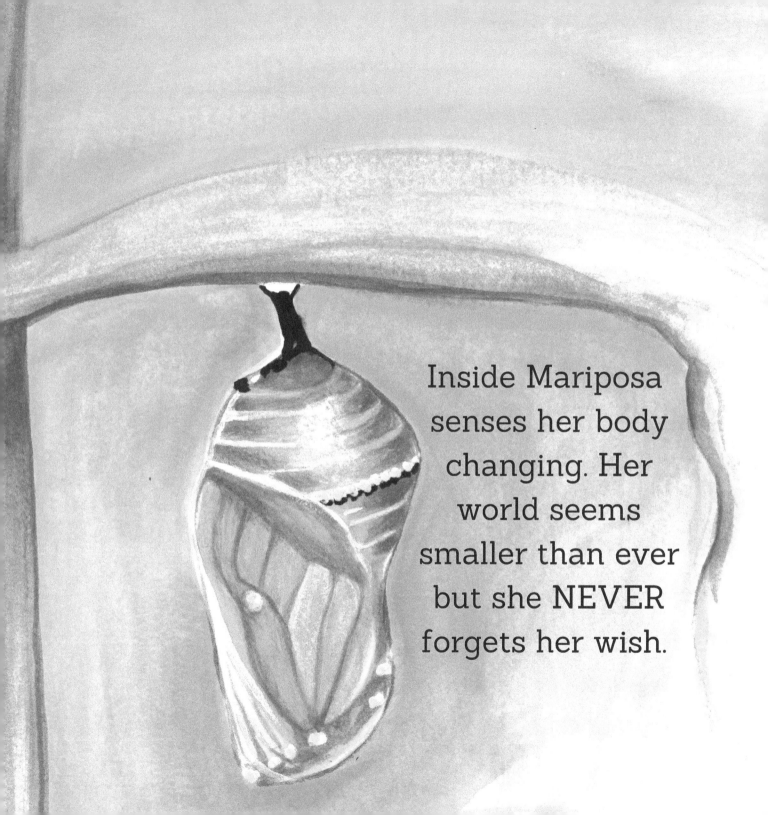

Inside Mariposa senses her body changing. Her world seems smaller than ever but she NEVER forgets her wish.

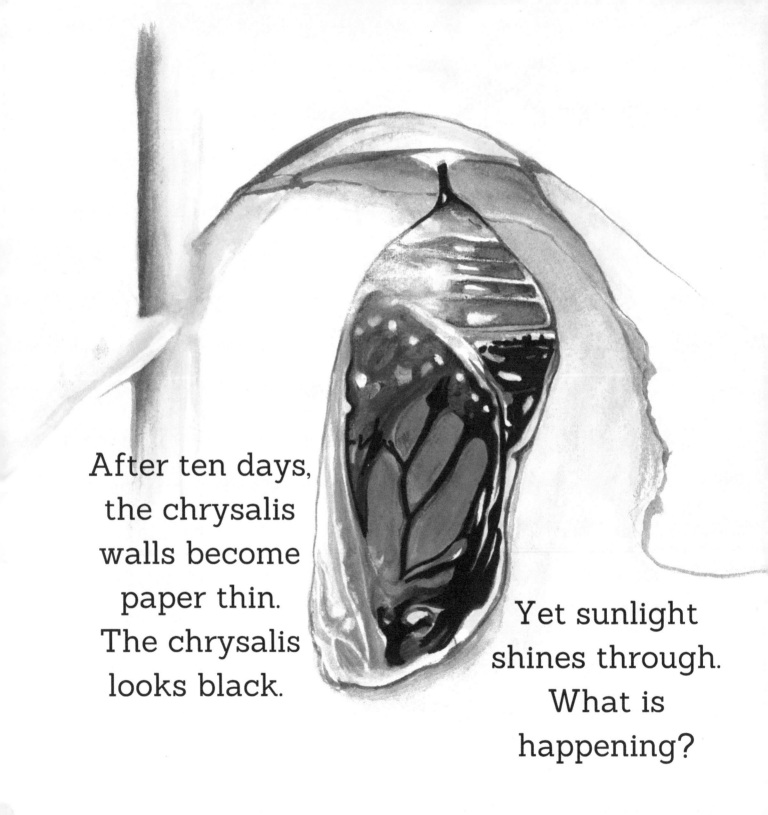

After ten days, the chrysalis walls become paper thin. The chrysalis looks black.

Yet sunlight shines through. What is happening?

Mariposa turns and twists.

Suddenly the chrysalis cracks open
and she uncurls herself. Mariposa
has been **transformed**.

Instead of inching about on many short feet, Mariposa walks on wire-like legs. Her eyes see more clearly. Her mouth is a long curly straw that she unrolls to sip nectar from flowers.

Most amazing are four delicate
orange and black wings. Once
her wings expand and dry,
Mariposa
discovers that
waving
them lifts
her body
into the air.

The new butterfly's heart pumps fluid into its wings causing its body to shrink and its wings to grow and flatten.

At first Mariposa's flying is unsteady and weak. She soon masters her new wings so she can flutter and glide.

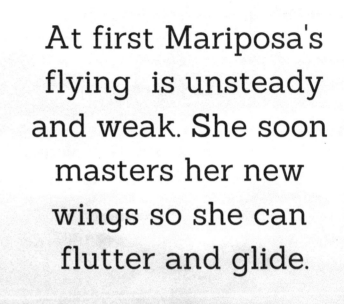

Now Mariposa's body has completed all its changes. She is an adult monarch butterfly.

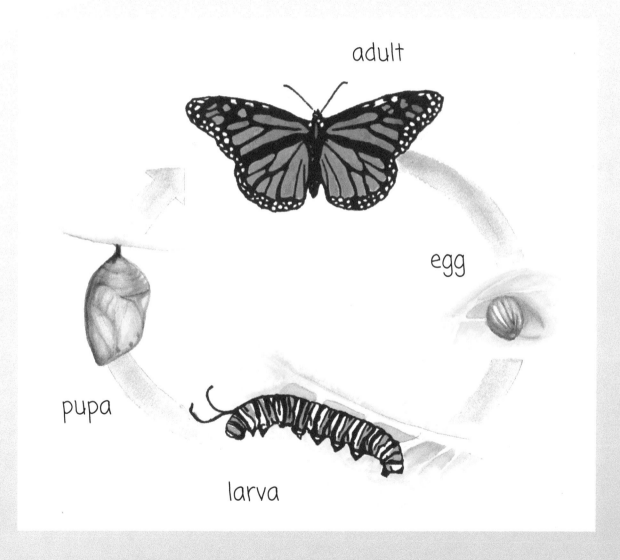

adult

egg

larva

pupa

Mariposa has become one of the most enchanting creatures on earth. She is colorful, graceful, and beautiful.

Mariposa waves goodbye to the milkweed plant and the meadow as she soars into the sky.

On her travels, Mariposa will fly over grassy prairies, rolling mountains, and enormous lakes.

She will taste the sweet nectar
of flowers and drink water from
soup-like puddles.

Eventually, Mariposa will choose
a mate. Then, on the bottom
of milkweed leaves, she
will lay tiny eggs.

More monarch caterpillars will hatch.
Each will have its own wishes for
journeys and explorations.

The Internet offers a wealth of monarch butterfly information. These websites can get you started.

Monarch Watch: education, conservation, research
  https://monarchwatch.org

Journey North: keep track of monarch migration
  https://journeynorth.org/monarchs

**Monarch Live: a distance learning adventure
                with many links**
  https://monarch.pwnet.org/trc/links.php

The Children's Butterfly Site
  https://www.kidsbutterfly.org

CPSIA information can be obtained
at www.ICGtesting.com
Printed in the USA
JSHW010849160622
27059JS00006B/73